Fractions: Concepts and Problem Solving
Grade 3

Table of Contents

Fractions: Concepts and Problem Solving
Grade 3

Introduction

Helping students form an understanding of fractions is a challenging process. To best accomplish the task, educators must approach the subject in a way that is meaningful for students. Moreover, the National Council of Teachers of Mathematics (NCTM) indicates that "students should build their understanding of fractions as parts of a whole and as division." (*Principles and Standards for School Mathematics*, page 150.) *Fractions: Concepts and Problem Solving* serves as a companion to the classroom mathematics curriculum and encompasses many of the standards established by the NCTM for this grade level. (Refer to the correlation chart below.) The book is divided into four units: Concept Development, Computation, Problem Solving, and Enrichment. Each page targets a specific skill to help bolster students who need additional work in one area.

Unit 1: Concept Development
The pages in this unit use a variety of learning styles to help students understand the fundamental principles of fractions. Students identify fractions that are parts of wholes, parts of groups, and mixed numbers. They also compare and order fractions.

Unit 2: Computation
Here, students are introduced to the steps necessary to calculate fractional algorithms using visuals. Practice exercises use models to guide students. Toward the end of the page, students work the problems without models. Students work to find simplest form, to add and subtract fractions with like denominators, and to add and subtract fractions with unlike denominators.

Unit 3: Problem Solving
Students work word and real-life application problems to further develop skills in fractions. They work with patterns, pictographs, circle graphs, and with time to find fractional relationships. They also explore basic probability.

Unit 4: Enrichment
To challenge and extend learning, students explore basic algebra principles, decimals, and money as they relate to fractions.

Special Note
We encourage the use of manipulatives for acquisition of skills with fractions. Examples include, but are not limited to, the following: Fraction Bars®, Fraction Tiles®, Fraction Builder® Strips, Rainbow Fraction Circles and Squares®, Fraction Stax®, and Fraction Burger®.

Notes

Assessment
There are two kinds of assessment pages.
- On pages 5 and 6 is a general assessment which covers important fraction skills appropriate for third grade. It can be given as a pretest to gauge students' knowledge of multiplication and division. Later in the year, the same test can be administered to determine students' understanding, progress, and achievement.
- The first three units also have an assessment. They can be administered at any time during the unit as a pretest, review, or posttest for specific fraction concepts.

NCTM Standards Correlation
The NCTM Standards Correlation chart below identifies a variety of mathematics standards that are appropriate for the study of fractions.

Fraction Table
A Fraction Table can be found on page 3. Students can use the graphic organizer to quickly identify and compare fractions. You may wish to make 2 photocopies for each student. One copy can be cut apart and used as fractions strips.

Fraction Circles
Fractions circles representing basic fractions are on page 4. Make a copy for each student. Students can cut them apart and use the circles as manipulatives while they work. You may wish to provide envelopes for students to store cut pieces.

NCTM Standards Correlation

Number and Operations: 5, 6, 7, 9, 10, 11, 12, 13, 14, 15, 16, 17, 18, 19, 20, 21, 22, 23, 24, 25, 26, 27, 28, 29, 30, 31, 32, 33, 34, 35, 36, 38, 39, 40, 41, 42, 43, 45, 46

Algebra: 5, 6, 7, 14, 15, 16, 17, 34, 36, 37, 38, 43, 44

Geometry: 5, 6, 7, 8, 9, 10, 11, 12, 13, 17, 18, 19, 20, 36, 37

Measurement: 8, 9, 10, 16, 26, 34, 35, 38, 39, 41, 44, 46

Data Analysis and Probability: 40, 41, 42, 44

Problem Solving: 5, 6, 7, 13, 14, 15, 16, 17, 19, 20, 21, 26, 34, 35, 36, 37, 38, 39, 40, 41, 42, 43, 44, 45, 46

Name _____ Date _____

Fraction Table

| 1 | $\frac{1}{2}$ | $\frac{1}{3}$ | $\frac{1}{4}$ | $\frac{1}{5}$ | $\frac{1}{6}$ | $\frac{1}{7}$ | $\frac{1}{8}$ | $\frac{1}{9}$ | $\frac{1}{10}$ | $\frac{1}{11}$ | $\frac{1}{12}$ |

Fraction Table

Fractions 3, SV 3406-1

Fraction Circles

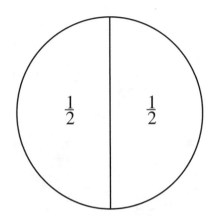

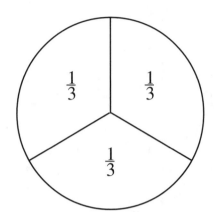

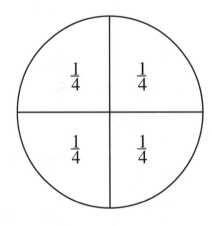

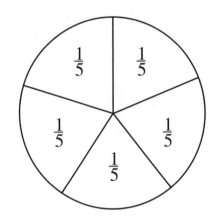

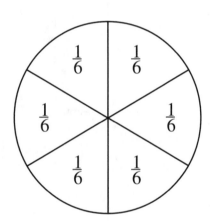

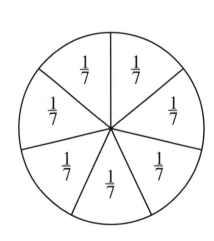

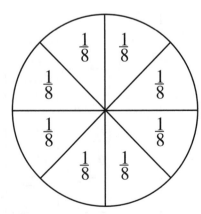

General Assessment

Directions

Darken the circle by the correct answer.

1. Which figure is $\frac{3}{4}$ shaded?

  Ⓐ A
  Ⓑ B
  Ⓒ C
  Ⓓ D

A   B   C   D

2. What fraction shows how many banners are white?

  Ⓐ $\frac{1}{2}$
  Ⓑ $\frac{1}{4}$
  Ⓒ $\frac{1}{3}$
  Ⓓ $\frac{1}{5}$

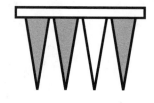

3. Which fraction shows how much one part of this sandwich equals?

  Ⓐ $\frac{1}{2}$
  Ⓑ $\frac{1}{3}$
  Ⓒ $\frac{1}{4}$
  Ⓓ $\frac{1}{5}$

4. What fraction tells how many parts of the circle are shaded?

  Ⓐ three tenths
  Ⓑ eight tenths
  Ⓒ five tenths
  Ⓓ six tenths

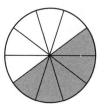

5. Look at the clock. What will be the time in half an hour?

  Ⓐ 4:15
  Ⓑ 3:30
  Ⓒ 4:45
  Ⓓ 4:30

6. What is the simplest form of $\frac{2}{4}$?

  Ⓐ $\frac{1}{3}$
  Ⓑ $\frac{1}{5}$
  Ⓒ $\frac{1}{2}$
  Ⓓ $\frac{2}{3}$

7. What is the mixed number for $\frac{8}{3}$?

  Ⓐ $\frac{3}{8}$
  Ⓑ $1\frac{2}{3}$
  Ⓒ $2\frac{2}{3}$
  Ⓓ $3\frac{1}{8}$

8. What fraction is equivalent to $\frac{2}{6}$?

  Ⓐ $\frac{1}{3}$
  Ⓑ $\frac{6}{2}$
  Ⓒ $\frac{1}{4}$
  Ⓓ $\frac{4}{8}$

Go on to the next page.

General Assessment, p. 2

9. $\frac{3}{8}$
$+ \frac{3}{8}$

Ⓐ $\frac{1}{8}$
Ⓑ $\frac{1}{2}$
Ⓒ $\frac{2}{3}$
Ⓓ $\frac{3}{4}$

10. $\frac{5}{9}$
$- \frac{2}{9}$

Ⓐ $\frac{2}{9}$
Ⓑ $\frac{1}{3}$
Ⓒ $\frac{2}{6}$
Ⓓ $\frac{7}{9}$

11. $2\frac{1}{3}$
$+ 1\frac{1}{3}$

Ⓐ 1
Ⓑ $2\frac{2}{3}$
Ⓒ $3\frac{1}{3}$
Ⓓ $3\frac{2}{3}$

12. $3\frac{3}{4}$
$- 1\frac{1}{4}$

Ⓐ $2\frac{1}{2}$
Ⓑ $2\frac{4}{4}$
Ⓒ $3\frac{1}{2}$
Ⓓ $3\frac{2}{4}$

13. Tom cut a pizza into 8 pieces. He ate 3 pieces. How much of the pizza is left?

Ⓐ $\frac{2}{8}$
Ⓑ $\frac{3}{8}$
Ⓒ $\frac{5}{8}$
Ⓓ $\frac{3}{4}$

14. How many inches are there between point B and point A?

Ⓐ $1\frac{1}{2}$ inches
Ⓑ 3 inches
Ⓒ 1 inch
Ⓓ $2\frac{1}{2}$ inches

15. Which figure shows $\frac{19}{100}$ shaded?

Ⓐ   Ⓑ

Ⓒ   Ⓓ

16. Which muffin pan is $\frac{1}{2}$ empty?

Ⓐ   Ⓑ

Ⓒ   Ⓓ

Unit 1 Assessment

Directions

Write a fraction for each model.

1.

_____

2.

_____

3.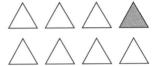

What part is shaded?

_____

4.

What part of the group of frogs
is on the log? _____

5.

_____

6.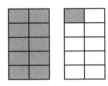

_____

Directions

Compare. Write <, >, or =.

7. $\frac{5}{6}$ ◯ $\frac{2}{3}$

8. $\frac{3}{5}$ ◯ $\frac{3}{8}$

Directions

Look at the first figure. Circle the figure that shows an equivalent fraction. Then, write the equivalent fractions.

9.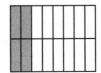

_____

Name _____ Date _____

Equal Parts

You can draw lines to divide a figure into parts. If all the parts are the same, they are equal.

equal   not equal

Directions

Draw a circle around the figures that have equal parts.

1.

2.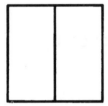

3.

4.

5.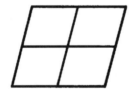

6.

7.

8.

Understanding Fraction Parts

A figure can be divided many ways. Sometimes, the parts are equal. Sometimes, the parts are not equal. If the parts are equal, count the number of equal parts.

2 equal parts   **3 equal parts**   **4 equal parts**   **0 equal parts**

Directions

Write the number of equal parts.

1.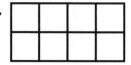

2.

3.

_____   _____   _____

4.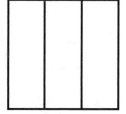

5.

6.

_____   _____   _____

Exploring Fractions

A fraction names equal parts of a whole.

Example: What part of the circle is shaded?

There are 3 parts shaded. $\boxed{3}$
There are 4 equal parts. $\boxed{4}$

So, 3 out of 4 parts are shaded.

Three fourths of the circle is shaded.

Directions

What part is shaded? Write the fraction.

1.

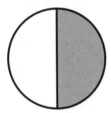

$$\frac{\text{shaded parts}}{\text{total parts}} = \frac{\Box}{\Box}$$

2.

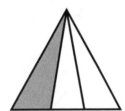

$$\frac{\text{shaded parts}}{\text{total parts}} = \frac{\Box}{\Box}$$

3.

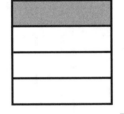

$$\frac{\text{shaded parts}}{\text{total parts}} = \frac{\Box}{\Box}$$

4.

$$\frac{\text{shaded parts}}{\text{total parts}} = \frac{\Box}{\Box}$$

5.

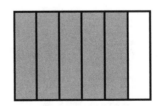

$$\frac{\text{shaded parts}}{\text{total parts}} = \frac{\Box}{\Box}$$

6.

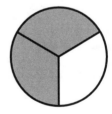

$$\frac{\text{shaded parts}}{\text{total parts}} = \frac{\Box}{\Box}$$

Writing Fractions

> A fraction names equal parts of a whole. The top number, or numerator, tells how many parts are being used. The bottom number, or denominator, tells how many equal parts there are in all.

Example: What fraction of the rhombus is shaded?

 $\dfrac{\text{parts shaded}}{\text{equal parts}}$ $\dfrac{3}{5}$ ← **numerator**
← **denominator**

So, $\frac{3}{5}$ of the figure is shaded. You read the fraction as three fifths or three out of five.

Directions

Write the fraction. Then, read the fraction.

1.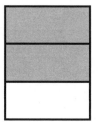

_____

2.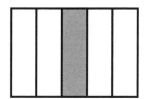

_____

3.

_____

4.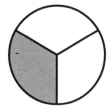

_____

5.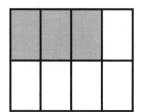

_____

6.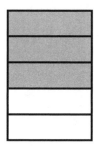

_____

Name _____ Date _____

Coloring Fractions

A fraction names equal parts of a whole. The top number is the numerator. The numerator tells how many parts are being used. The bottom number is the denominator. The denominator tells how many equal parts there are in all.

Example: What fraction of the circle is shaded?

$$\frac{\text{parts shaded}}{\text{equal parts}} \qquad \frac{2 \leftarrow \textbf{numerator}}{3 \leftarrow \textbf{denominator}}$$

Directions

Color the fraction.

1.

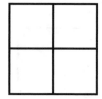

$\frac{1}{4}$

2.

$\frac{1}{3}$

3.

$\frac{1}{2}$

4.

$\frac{4}{6}$

5.

$\frac{5}{6}$

6.

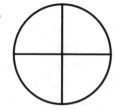

$\frac{2}{4}$

Important Fractions

A fraction shows parts of a whole. The top number is the numerator. The numerator tells how many parts are being used. The bottom number is the denominator. The denominator tells how many equal parts there are in all.

Directions

Color the fraction.

1. $\frac{1}{2}$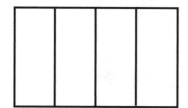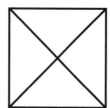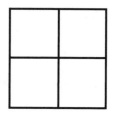

2. $\frac{1}{3}$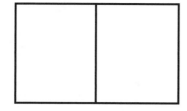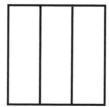

3. $\frac{1}{4}$

4. Tony ate $\frac{3}{4}$ of the pizza. Circle the part of the pizza Tony ate.

Name _____   Date _____

Part of a Group

A set of items can be divided into equal groups.

Example: What part of the group is shaded?

2 stars
1 star is shaded

4 stars
2 equal parts
1 part is shaded

8 stars
2 equal parts
1 part is shaded

Each picture shows 2 equal parts with 1 part shaded.

Directions

Look at each group. Write the parts.

1.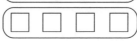

   __1__ part shaded
   _____ parts not shaded
   _____ equal parts

2.

   _____ part shaded
   _____ parts not shaded
   _____ equal parts

3.

   _____ part shaded
   _____ part not shaded
   _____ equal parts

4.

   _____ parts shaded
   _____ part not shaded
   _____ equal parts

Fractions of a Group

A fraction names equal parts of a group. The numerator tells how many parts are being used. The denominator tells how many parts in all.

Example: What fraction of the group is shaded?

shaded parts $\boxed{1}$ ← **numerator**

equal parts $\boxed{3}$ ← **denominator**

shaded parts $\boxed{3}$

equal parts $\boxed{6}$

(Directions)

Write the fraction.

1.

$\dfrac{\text{shaded parts}}{\text{total parts}}$ = $\dfrac{\boxed{}}{\boxed{}}$

2.

$\dfrac{\text{shaded parts}}{\text{total parts}}$ = $\dfrac{\boxed{}}{\boxed{}}$

3.

$\dfrac{\boxed{}}{\boxed{}}$

4.

$\dfrac{\boxed{}}{\boxed{}}$

5. Janet's cat had kittens.
   What fraction of the kittens are gray?

Estimating Fractions

An **estimate** is a guess. You can use fractions to estimate how much there is of something when you do not need an exact answer. Fraction circles can help you make an estimate.

Example: About how much pizza is left?

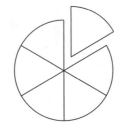

So, about $\frac{1}{6}$ of a pizza is left.

Directions

Circle the best estimate.

1.

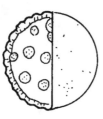

$\frac{1}{2}$ $\frac{1}{4}$ $\frac{1}{8}$

2.

$\frac{1}{2}$ $\frac{2}{3}$ $\frac{1}{8}$

3.

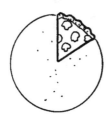

$\frac{1}{4}$ $\frac{3}{4}$ $\frac{1}{2}$

4.

$\frac{2}{3}$ $\frac{1}{2}$ $\frac{1}{4}$

5.

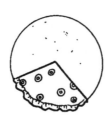

$\frac{1}{2}$ $\frac{3}{10}$ $\frac{9}{10}$

6.

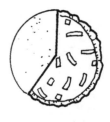

$\frac{1}{10}$ $\frac{5}{8}$ $\frac{1}{8}$

Whole Fractions

A fraction shows an equal number of parts. A fraction is used to show an amount smaller than 1. But a fraction can show a whole amount, too. It can show the number 1.

Example: Count the fraction parts.

  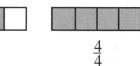

$$\frac{1}{4} \qquad \frac{2}{4} \qquad \frac{3}{4} \qquad \frac{4}{4}$$

So, $\frac{4}{4}$ is the same as 1 whole, or $\frac{4}{4} = 1$.

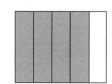

Directions

Write a fraction to describe each shaded part.

1.   **2.**

___   ___   ___   ___   ___   ___   ___   ___   ___

3.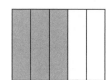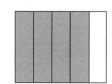

___   ___   ___   ___   ___

Directions

Write a fraction that names the shaded part.

4. 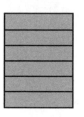   ___   **5.** 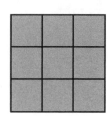   ___   **6.** 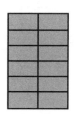   ___

Comparing Fractions

Sometimes, you will need to compare fractions. You will need to find if one fraction is more than, less than, or the same as another fraction. Fraction bars can help you compare fractions.

Example 1: Compare $\frac{1}{3}$ and $\frac{2}{3}$.

$\frac{1}{3}$ is less than $\frac{2}{3}$.
So, $\frac{1}{3} < \frac{2}{3}$.

Example 2: Compare $\frac{3}{4}$ and $\frac{2}{4}$.

$\frac{3}{4}$ is more than $\frac{2}{4}$.
So, $\frac{3}{4} > \frac{2}{4}$.

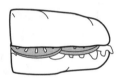

Directions

Compare. Write <, >, or =.

1.

$\frac{3}{5} \bigcirc \frac{4}{5}$

2.

$\frac{2}{3} \bigcirc \frac{4}{6}$

3.

$\frac{3}{4} \bigcirc \frac{1}{2}$

4.

$\frac{4}{8} \bigcirc \frac{1}{2}$

5.

$\frac{3}{5} \bigcirc \frac{3}{8}$

6.

$\frac{2}{5} \bigcirc \frac{4}{5}$

Equivalent Fractions

Fractions that name the same amount are called **equivalent fractions**. Fraction bars can help you find equivalent fractions.

Example: Are $\frac{1}{2}$, $\frac{2}{4}$, and $\frac{3}{6}$ equivalent fractions?

So, $\frac{1}{2} = \frac{2}{4} = \frac{3}{6}$.

Directions Color to show equivalent fractions. Then, write the equivalent fraction.

1.
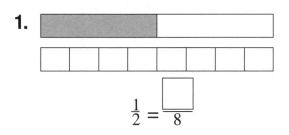

$\frac{1}{2} = \frac{\boxed{}}{8}$

2.
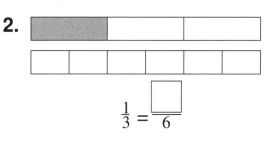

$\frac{1}{3} = \frac{\boxed{}}{6}$

3.
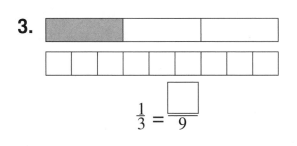

$\frac{1}{3} = \frac{\boxed{}}{9}$

4.
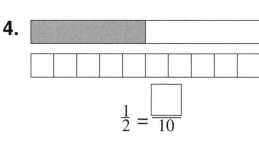

$\frac{1}{2} = \frac{\boxed{}}{10}$

Directions Use fraction bars. Write the equivalent fraction.

5. $\frac{1}{4} = \frac{\boxed{}}{8}$ **6.** $\frac{2}{5} = \frac{\boxed{}}{10}$ **7.** $\frac{1}{3} = \frac{\boxed{}}{9}$ **8.** $\frac{2}{4} = \frac{\boxed{}}{2}$

Ordering Fractions

Sometimes, you will need to order a set of fractions. To do this, compare 2 fractions. Write them in order using > or <. Then, compare the other fraction. Fraction bars can help you.

Example: Order the fractions from least to greatest.

$\frac{2}{5}$

$\frac{4}{6}$

$\frac{3}{4}$

$\frac{2}{5} < \frac{4}{6}$

$\frac{4}{6} < \frac{3}{4}$

So, $\frac{2}{5} < \frac{4}{6} < \frac{3}{4}$.

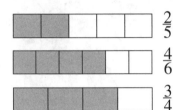 **Directions**

Write the fractions in order from least to greatest.

1. $\frac{6}{8}$

$\frac{3}{8}$

$\frac{5}{8}$

_____

2. $\frac{2}{6}$

$\frac{5}{6}$

$\frac{1}{6}$

_____

3. $\frac{2}{3}$

$\frac{7}{9}$

$\frac{2}{5}$

_____

4. $\frac{5}{8}$

$\frac{9}{10}$

$\frac{1}{4}$

_____

Mixed Numbers

> A **mixed number** has a whole number and a fraction.

Example 1:

1 whole apple + $\frac{1}{2}$ of another apple

$1 + \frac{1}{2} = 1\frac{1}{2}$ apples

Example 2:

2 whole pizzas + $\frac{5}{8}$ of another pizza

$2 + \frac{5}{8} = 2\frac{5}{8}$ pizzas

(Directions) **Complete. Then, write the mixed number.**

1.

_____ whole + $\dfrac{\square}{\square}$ = $\square\dfrac{\square}{\square}$

2.

_____ wholes + $\dfrac{\square}{\square}$ = $\square\dfrac{\square}{\square}$

3.

_____ wholes + $\dfrac{\square}{\square}$ = $\square\dfrac{\square}{\square}$

4.

_____ wholes + $\dfrac{\square}{\square}$ = $\square\dfrac{\square}{\square}$

(Directions) **Write the mixed number that names the shaded part.**

5.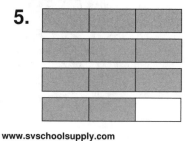

_____

6.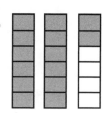

_____

Unit 2 Assessment

Directions

Write each fraction in simplest form.

1. $\frac{3}{6}$ = _____

2. $\frac{8}{12}$ = _____

3. $\frac{6}{8}$ = _____

Directions

Write the mixed number.

4. $\frac{8}{3}$ = _____

5. $\frac{11}{9}$ = _____

6. $\frac{13}{4}$ = _____

Directions

Find the common denominator.

7. $\frac{1}{2}$ and $\frac{2}{3}$

8. $\frac{1}{4}$ and $\frac{3}{8}$

_____   _____

Directions

Add or subtract. Reduce to simplest form.

9. $\begin{array}{r} \frac{1}{5} \\ + \frac{3}{5} \\ \hline \end{array}$

10. $\begin{array}{r} \frac{3}{6} \\ - \frac{1}{6} \\ \hline \end{array}$

11. $\begin{array}{r} \frac{1}{8} \\ + \frac{3}{8} \\ \hline \end{array}$

12. $\begin{array}{r} \frac{7}{10} \\ - \frac{6}{10} \\ \hline \end{array}$

13. $\begin{array}{r} \frac{1}{2} \\ + \frac{1}{4} \\ \hline \end{array}$

14. $\begin{array}{r} \frac{3}{4} \\ - \frac{1}{8} \\ \hline \end{array}$

15. $\frac{4}{5} - \frac{2}{10}$ = _____

16. $\frac{1}{2} + \frac{2}{4}$ = _____

Simplest Form

A fraction is in **simplest form** when you write the smallest equivalent fraction. You can divide the numerator and denominator of a fraction by the same number to reduce the fraction to simplest form.

Example: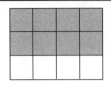

Step 1: Find a number that will divide evenly into the numerator and denominator.

$$\frac{8}{12} = \frac{8 \div 2}{12 \div 2} = \frac{4}{6}$$

Step 2: Repeat Step 1 until the only number that will divide both the numerator and denominator evenly is 1.

$$\frac{4}{6} = \frac{4 \div 2}{6 \div 2} = \frac{2}{3}$$

So, $\frac{8}{12}$ in simplest form is $\frac{2}{3}$, or $\frac{8}{12} = \frac{2}{3}$.

Directions

Write each fraction in simplest form.

1.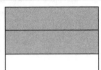

$$\frac{2}{6} = \frac{2 \div 2}{6 \div 2} = \boxed{}$$

2.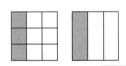

$$\frac{3}{9} = \frac{3 \div 3}{9 \div 3} = \boxed{}$$

3.

$$\frac{3}{12} = \boxed{}$$

4.

$$\frac{8}{10} = \boxed{}$$

Improper Fractions

An **improper fraction** is a fraction in which the numerator is larger than the denominator. You can change an improper fraction to a mixed number by dividing.

Example: Write $\frac{15}{4}$ as a mixed number.

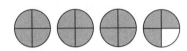

Step 1:
Write the fraction as a division problem. Write the numerator as a dividend. Write the denominator as a divisor. Solve.

$$\text{denominator} \rightarrow 4\overline{)15} \leftarrow \text{numerator}$$
$$\underline{-12}$$
$$3$$

Step 2:
Write the quotient as a mixed number. Write any remainder as a fraction. Write the remainder as a numerator. Write the divisor as the denominator.

$$3\frac{3}{4} \begin{array}{l} \leftarrow \text{remainder} \\ \leftarrow \text{divisor} \end{array}$$
$$4\overline{)15}$$
$$\underline{-12}$$
$$3$$

So, $\frac{15}{4} = 3\frac{3}{4}$.

Directions

Write each fraction as a mixed number.

1.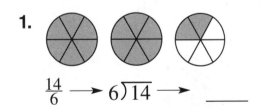

$$\frac{14}{6} \longrightarrow 6\overline{)14} \longrightarrow \underline{\quad}$$

2.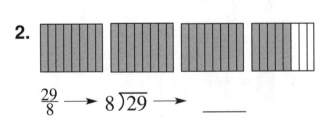

$$\frac{29}{8} \longrightarrow 8\overline{)29} \longrightarrow \underline{\quad}$$

3. $\frac{17}{4} \longrightarrow 4\overline{)17} \longrightarrow \underline{\quad}$

4. $\frac{20}{3} \longrightarrow 3\overline{)20} \longrightarrow \underline{\quad}$

Finding Part of a Group

Fractions can name part of a group. You can use division to calculate the fraction of a group.

Example: Find $\frac{1}{3}$ of 12.

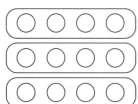

Step 1: Write the whole number as a fraction.

$12 = \frac{12}{1}$

Step 2: Multiply the numerators. Multiply the denominators. Write the products as an improper fraction.

$\frac{1}{3} \times \frac{12}{1} = \frac{1 \times 12}{3 \times 1} = \frac{12}{3}$

Step 3: Rename the improper fraction as a mixed number by dividing.

$12 \div 3 = 4$

So, $\frac{1}{3}$ of 12 is 4.

Directions

Solve.

1. $\frac{1}{2}$ of 8 = _____

To find $\frac{1}{2}$, divide by 2.

$8 \div 2 =$ _____

2. $\frac{1}{3}$ of 9 = _____

○ ○ ○
○ ○ ○
○ ○ ○

To find $\frac{1}{3}$, divide by 3.

$9 \div 3 =$ _____

3. $\frac{1}{3}$ of 6 = _____

○ ○ ○
○ ○ ○

To find $\frac{1}{3}$, divide by 3.

$6 \div 3 =$ _____

4. $\frac{1}{4}$ of 12 = _____

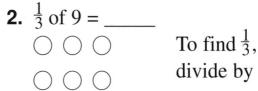

To find $\frac{1}{4}$, divide by 4.

$12 \div 4 =$ _____

Estimating Sums and Differences

> You can estimate the sums and differences of fractions.
> Fraction bars can help you.

Example 1: $\frac{2}{3} + \frac{5}{6} = \square$ **Example 2:** $\frac{5}{6} - \frac{2}{3} = \square$

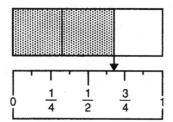   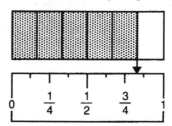

$\frac{2}{3}$ is about $\frac{1}{2}$. $\frac{5}{6}$ is about 1.

Think: $\frac{2}{3}$ is close to $\frac{1}{2}$.   **Think:** $\frac{5}{6}$ is close to 1.

$\frac{5}{6}$ is close to 1. $\frac{2}{3}$ is close to $\frac{1}{2}$.

$\frac{1}{2} + 1 = 1\frac{1}{2}$ So, $\frac{5}{6} - \frac{2}{3}$ is about $\frac{1}{2}$.

So, $\frac{2}{3} + \frac{5}{6}$ is about $1\frac{1}{2}$.

(Directions) Use the fraction bar to help you estimate. Write *about 0, about $\frac{1}{2}$, or about 1.*

1.   **2.**   **3.**

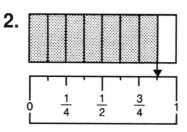

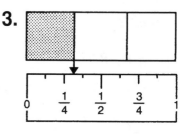

$\frac{1}{6}$ is _____. $\frac{7}{8}$ is _____. $\frac{1}{3}$ is _____.

(Directions) Use the fraction bars on this worksheet to help you estimate each sum or difference. Write *about 0, about $\frac{1}{2}$, about 1, or about $1\frac{1}{2}$.*

4. $\frac{1}{6} + \frac{7}{8} = \square$ **5.** $\frac{7}{8} - \frac{1}{3} = \square$ **6.** $\frac{5}{6} - \frac{1}{6} = \square$ **7.** $\frac{7}{8} + \frac{2}{3} = \square$

_____   _____   _____   _____

Adding Fractions with Like Denominators

When you add like fractions, add only the numerators.

Example: $\frac{2}{6} + \frac{2}{6} = \boxed{}$

 + =

$\frac{2 \text{ parts shaded}}{6 \text{ total parts}}$ + $\frac{2 \text{ parts shaded}}{6 \text{ total parts}}$ = $\frac{4 \text{ parts shaded}}{6 \text{ total parts}}$

Step 1: Add the numerators. $2 + 2 = 4$

Step 2: Write the denominator. $\frac{4}{6}$

Step 3: Reduce to simplest form if you can. $\frac{4}{6} = \frac{4 \div 2}{6 \div 2} = \frac{2}{3}$

So, $\frac{2}{6} + \frac{2}{6} = \frac{2}{3}$.

Directions

Color the correct number of parts. Then, solve.

1.

$\frac{1}{4} + \frac{2}{4} = $ _____

2.

$\frac{3}{8} + \frac{4}{8} = $ _____

3.

$\frac{2}{10} + \frac{5}{10} = $ _____

Directions

Add. Show how you add the numerators. Reduce to simplest form.

4. $\frac{2}{6} + \frac{2}{6} = \frac{2+2}{6} = $ _____

5. $\frac{3}{7} + \frac{3}{7} = $ _____

6. $\frac{1}{8} + \frac{3}{8} = $ _____

7. $\frac{2}{5} + \frac{2}{5} = $ _____

Adding Mixed Numbers with Like Denominators

When adding mixed numbers, first add the fractions and then add the whole numbers.

Example:

$$7\frac{2}{6}$$
$$+\ 4\frac{2}{6}$$

Step 1: Add the fractions.

$$7\frac{2}{6}$$
$$+\ 4\frac{2}{6}$$
$$\overline{\frac{4}{6}}$$

Step 2: Add the whole numbers.

$$7\frac{2}{6}$$
$$+\ 4\frac{2}{6}$$
$$\overline{11\frac{4}{6}}$$

Step 3: Reduce to simplest form.

$$7\frac{2}{6}$$
$$+\ 4\frac{2}{6}$$
$$\overline{11\frac{4}{6}} = 11\frac{2}{3}$$

So, the sum is $11\frac{2}{3}$.

If the problem is written horizontally, you can rewrite the problem vertically and then follow the steps above.

Write $3\frac{1}{7} + 4\frac{5}{7} = \square$ →

$$3\frac{1}{7}$$
$$+\ 4\frac{5}{7}$$

$$3\frac{1}{7}$$
$$+\ 4\frac{5}{7}$$
$$\overline{7\frac{6}{7}}$$

Directions

Add. Reduce to simplest form.

1. $5\frac{2}{9}$
$+\ 2\frac{4}{9}$

2. $3\frac{1}{6}$
$+\ 7\frac{3}{6}$

3. $5\frac{3}{10}$
$+\ \frac{6}{10}$

4. 7
$+\ 1\frac{3}{8}$

5. $5\frac{2}{8} + 6\frac{3}{8} =$ _____

6. $4 + \frac{2}{3} =$ _____

7. $3\frac{4}{7} + 2\frac{3}{7} =$ _____

8. $6\frac{1}{4} + \frac{2}{4} =$ _____

Subtracting Fractions with Like Denominators

When you subtract like fractions, subtract only the numerators.

Example: $\frac{6}{8} - \frac{2}{8} = \boxed{}$

 − =

$$\frac{6 \text{ parts shaded}}{8 \text{ total parts}} - \frac{2 \text{ parts shaded}}{8 \text{ total parts}} = \frac{4 \text{ parts shaded}}{8 \text{ total parts}}$$

Step 1: Subtract the numerators. $6 - 2 = 4$

Step 2: Write the denominator. $\frac{4}{8}$

Step 3: Reduce to simplest form if you can. $\frac{4}{8} = \frac{4 \div 4}{8 \div 4} = \frac{1}{2}$

So, $\frac{6}{8} - \frac{2}{8} = \frac{1}{2}$.

Directions

Cross out the correct number of parts. Then, complete.

1.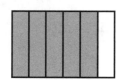

$\frac{5}{6} - \frac{3}{6} = $ _____

2.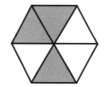

$\frac{3}{6} - \frac{2}{6} = $ _____

Directions

Subtract. Show how you subtract the numerators. Reduce to simplest form.

3. $\frac{5}{6} - \frac{1}{6} = \frac{5-1}{6} = $ _____

4. $\frac{6}{7} - \frac{3}{7} = $ _____

5. $\frac{7}{8} - \frac{4}{8} = $ _____

6. $\frac{4}{5} - \frac{2}{5} = $ _____

Subtracting Mixed Numbers with Like Denominators

When subtracting mixed numbers, first subtract the fractions and then subtract the whole numbers.

Example:

$$8\frac{5}{6}$$
$$-\ 1\frac{3}{6}$$

Step 1:
Subtract the fractions.

$$8\frac{5}{6}$$
$$-\ 1\frac{3}{6}$$
$$\frac{2}{6}$$

Step 2:
Subtract the whole numbers.

$$8\frac{5}{6}$$
$$-\ 1\frac{3}{6}$$
$$7\frac{2}{6}$$

Step 3:
Reduce to simplest form.

$$8\frac{5}{6}$$
$$-\ 1\frac{3}{6}$$
$$7\frac{2}{6} = 7\frac{1}{3}$$

So, $8\frac{5}{6} - 1\frac{3}{6} = 7\frac{1}{3}$.

If the problem is written horizontally, you can rewrite the problem vertically and then follow the steps above.

Directions

Subtract. Reduce to simplest form.

1. $5\frac{4}{5}$
$-\ 1\frac{2}{5}$

2. $8\frac{6}{8}$
$-\ 3\frac{2}{8}$

3. $9\frac{8}{12}$
$-\ \frac{4}{12}$

4. $4\frac{5}{6}$
$-\ 3\frac{3}{6}$

5. $7\frac{8}{9}$
$-\ 6$

6. $9\frac{9}{10}$
$-\ 5\frac{2}{10}$

7. 8
$-\ 6\frac{1}{4}$

Common Denominators

Sometimes, it is necessary to find a **common denominator** when working with fractions. Fractions that have common denominators have the same denominator.

Example: Find the common denominator of $\frac{1}{2}$ and $\frac{1}{6}$.

Step 1: Write equivalent fractions so that the fractions have a common denominator. Work with the fraction that has the smallest denominator first. Try to find a fraction that has the same denominator of the second fraction.

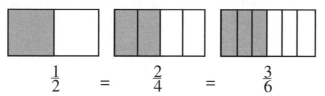

$$\frac{1}{2} \quad = \quad \frac{2}{4} \quad = \quad \frac{3}{6}$$

Step 2: Write the fractions with the same denominator.
$\frac{3}{6}$ and $\frac{1}{6}$

So, sixths is the common denominator of $\frac{1}{2}$ and $\frac{1}{6}$.

(Directions)

Use fraction bars to help you. Name the common denominator. Then, write the fractions with the common denominator.

1. $\frac{2}{5}$ and $\frac{7}{10}$

_____

2. $\frac{2}{3}$ and $\frac{5}{6}$

_____

3. $\frac{1}{6}$ and $\frac{5}{12}$

_____

4. $\frac{1}{3}$ and $\frac{4}{9}$

_____

5. $\frac{3}{8}$ and $\frac{1}{4}$

_____

6. $\frac{2}{3}$ and $\frac{4}{6}$

_____

Adding Fractions with Unlike Denominators

When adding fractions, remember to look at the denominators first. If they are not the same, find a common denominator.

Example: $\frac{3}{4} + \frac{1}{2} = \square$

Step 1:
Write equivalent fractions so that the fractions have a common denominator.

$$\frac{3}{4} \rightarrow \frac{3}{4}$$
$$+\frac{1}{2} \rightarrow \frac{2}{4}$$

Step 2:
Add the numerators. Write the sum with the same denominator.

$$\begin{array}{r} \frac{3}{4} \\ +\frac{2}{4} \\ \hline \frac{5}{4} \end{array}$$

Step 3:
Reduce to simplest form.

$$\begin{array}{r} \frac{3}{4} \\ +\frac{2}{4} \\ \hline \frac{5}{4} = 1\frac{1}{4} \end{array}$$

So, $\frac{3}{4} + \frac{1}{2} = 1\frac{1}{4}$.

Directions

Add. Use fraction bars. Reduce to simplest form.

1. $\frac{7}{10} \rightarrow \square$
   $+\frac{1}{2} \rightarrow \square$

2. $\frac{1}{9} \rightarrow \square$
   $+\frac{1}{3} \rightarrow \square$

3. $\frac{5}{8} \rightarrow \square$
   $+\frac{1}{4} \rightarrow \square$

4. $\frac{3}{4} \rightarrow \square$
   $+\frac{3}{8} \rightarrow \square$

5. $\quad\frac{1}{4}$
   $+\frac{6}{16}$

6. $\quad\frac{3}{5}$
   $+\frac{6}{10}$

Subtracting Fractions with Unlike Denominators

When subtracting fractions, remember to look at the denominators first. If they are not the same, find a common denominator.

Example: $\frac{5}{6} - \frac{1}{2} = \square$

Step 1:
Write equivalent fractions so that the fractions have a common denominator.

$$\frac{5}{6} \rightarrow \frac{5}{6}$$
$$-\frac{1}{2} \rightarrow \frac{3}{6}$$

Step 2:
Subtract the numerators. Write the difference with the same denominator.

$$\begin{array}{r}\frac{5}{6}\\-\frac{3}{6}\\\hline\frac{2}{6}\end{array}$$

Step 3:
Reduce to simplest form.

$$\begin{array}{r}\frac{5}{6}\\-\frac{3}{6}\\\hline\frac{2}{6}\end{array} = \frac{1}{3}$$

So, $\frac{5}{6} - \frac{1}{2} = \frac{1}{3}$.

(Directions)

Subtract. Use fraction bars. Reduce to simplest form.

1. $\frac{9}{16} \rightarrow \square$

   $-\frac{1}{4} \rightarrow \square$

2. $\frac{3}{4} \rightarrow \square$

   $-\frac{5}{8} \rightarrow \square$

3. $\frac{2}{4} \rightarrow \square$

   $-\frac{1}{8} \rightarrow \square$

4. $\frac{9}{12} \rightarrow \square$

   $-\frac{3}{4} \rightarrow \square$

5. $\begin{array}{r}\frac{8}{15}\\-\frac{2}{5}\end{array}$

6. $\begin{array}{r}\frac{1}{2}\\-\frac{2}{12}\end{array}$

Name _____   Date _____

Unit 3 Assessment

Directions

Solve.

1. A bowl of muffin batter contains $\frac{1}{3}$ cup of oil and $\frac{2}{3}$ cup of milk. Do the muffins have more oil or milk?

   _____

2. Joseph added $\frac{1}{4}$ cup of raisins and $\frac{1}{4}$ cup of chocolate chips to cookie dough. What fraction of a cup of both raisins and chips did Joseph add?

   _____

3. Shade to complete the pattern. What fraction did you shade?

   _____

4. Complete the pattern. Write the next 2 numbers.

   $\frac{1}{2}$, $\frac{2}{3}$, $\frac{3}{4}$, _____ , _____

5. John rides his bike from 2:00 until 2:30. For what fraction of an hour did John ride his bike?

   _____

6. How far did John jump?

   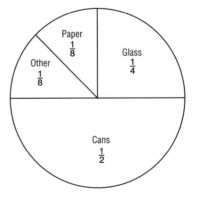

Directions

Use the graph to answer Exercises 7–8.

Trash Kim Picks Up

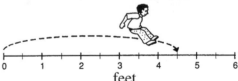

7. What fraction of the trash that Kim picked up was glass? _____

8. Did Kim pick up more cans or glass? How much more?

   _____

Word Problems

Directions Solve.

1. Sean spent $\frac{3}{7}$ of his allowance on a book and $\frac{2}{5}$ on a baseball. On which item did he spend more?

   _____

2. Tommy has finished $\frac{3}{4}$ of his math problems. What part of his math problems has Tommy not yet finished?

   _____

3. Joe and Todd bought a pizza that had 8 slices. They ate all but one slice. What fraction names the part of the pizza that they ate?

   _____

4. Shelly used $\frac{10}{3}$ cups of noodles to make a tuna-noodle dish. How many cups of noodles did she use? Write the answer as a mixed number.

   _____

5. A scout troop hiked along a trail. The scouts hiked $\frac{2}{8}$ of the way on the first day and $\frac{3}{8}$ of the way on the second day. What part of the trail did they hike?

   _____

6. Of the scout troop, $\frac{3}{12}$ slept in one tent and $\frac{4}{12}$ slept in another. The rest slept in a cabin. What part of the troop slept in tents?

   _____

7. Elena had $\frac{5}{6}$ of a box of pancake mix. She used $\frac{4}{6}$ of the box to make pancakes for breakfast. How much of the pancake mix was left?

   _____

8. Soon-Li had $\frac{4}{5}$ of a pitcher of orange juice. Her family drank $\frac{3}{5}$ of a pitcher of the juice. Was there close to no orange juice, $\frac{1}{2}$ pitcher, or a whole pitcher left?

   _____

Fraction Patterns

Directions

Answer the questions.

1.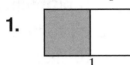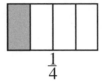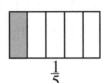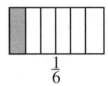

$$\frac{1}{2} \qquad \frac{1}{3} \qquad \frac{1}{4} \qquad \frac{1}{5} \qquad \frac{1}{6}$$

a. What is the pattern?

_____

b. What do you notice about the shaded parts?

_____

2.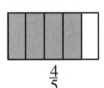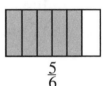

$$\frac{1}{2} \qquad \frac{2}{3} \qquad \frac{3}{4} \qquad \frac{4}{5} \qquad \frac{5}{6}$$

a. What is the pattern?

_____

b. What do you notice about the shaded parts?

_____

Directions

Complete the pattern.

3.

4.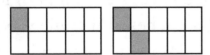

5. $\frac{1}{4}, \frac{2}{8}, \frac{3}{12},$ _____

6. $\frac{1}{2}, 1, 1\frac{1}{2}, 2,$ _____

7. $\frac{5}{6}, \frac{4}{6}, \frac{3}{6},$ _____

8. $\frac{1}{2}, \frac{2}{5}, \frac{3}{8}, \frac{4}{11},$ _____

Shape Patterns

Directions

Shade the last, unshaded shape in a way to continue the pattern the first shapes start. Tell how many parts make up the last shape. Then, tell how many parts you have shaded.

1. 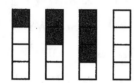   2.

_____   _____

3.

_____

4.

_____

5.

_____

6.

_____

Time

The clock is $\frac{1}{4}$ shaded. It shows 15 minutes, or a quarter hour.

The clock shows $\frac{1}{2}$ shaded. It shows 30 minutes, or a half hour.

The clock shows $\frac{3}{4}$ shaded. It shows 45 minutes, or three quarters of an hour.

Directions

Draw the minute hand to show the start and end times. Write the fraction of an hour that has passed.

Start	End	Fraction of Time

1.

 1:30

 1:45

_____

2.

 6:45

7:30

_____

3.

 10:30

11:00

_____

4.

 5:30

6:00

_____

Measurement

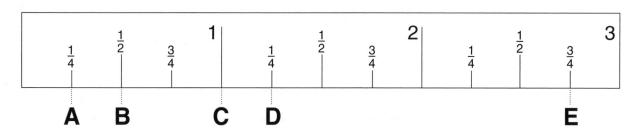

This is a section of a customary ruler. It measures length. The markings on the ruler divide it into inches. Each inch is divided into halves and quarters.

- The **A** above shows $\frac{1}{4}$ of 1 inch.

- The **B** above shows $\frac{1}{2}$ of 1 inch.

- The **C** above shows 1 inch exactly.

- The **D** above shows 1 and $\frac{1}{4}$ inches.
  It is past the 1-inch mark, so it is $1\frac{1}{4}$ inches.

- What do you think the **E** shows? Is it greater than 1 inch? Is it greater than 2 inches? How many quarter inches does it show? If you guessed $2\frac{3}{4}$ inches, you are correct.

Directions

Look at the ruler below. For each letter, write the measurement that is shown.

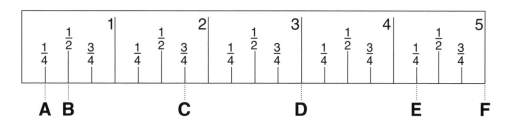

A. _____ B. _____ C. _____ D. _____ E. _____ F. _____

Name _____ Date _____

Pictographs

A **pictograph** uses pictures to show information. Each symbol stands
for a certain number of people or things. When part of a symbol shows,
you need to guess what fraction of the number is shown.

The pictograph shows the favorite
outside activities of the students in
Mr. Metz's third-grade class.

Favorite Outside Activities for Mr. Metz's Third Grade Class	
Tennis	☼ ☼ ◁
Swimming	☼ ☼ ☼ ☼
Golfing	☼ ◁
Biking	☼ ☼ ☼ ◁
Hiking	☼ ☼ ☼

Each ☼ stands for 2.

Directions

Use the pictograph to answer the questions.

1. How many students does each ☼ stand for? _____

2. How many students does each ◁ stand for? _____

3. What sport did most students like? _____

4. What sport did the least students like? _____

5. How many students are in Mr. Metz's class? _____

6. Write the fraction of students who like each sport.

   a. tennis _____   **b.** swimming _____

   c. golfing _____   **d.** biking _____

   e. hiking _____

Circle Graphs

A **circle graph** looks like it sounds. Each slice of the circle is a piece of information included in the circle. The size of each piece shows its relationship to the whole and to each other piece in the circle. A circle graph can use fractions to show data. The sum of the fractional pieces must equal 1.

The circle graph shows the fractional amount of ingredients used to make punch.

Punch for a Crowd

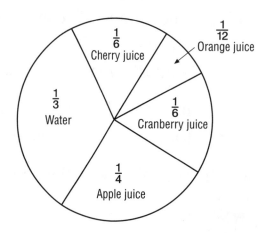

Directions

Use the graph to answer the questions.

1. What fraction of apple juice is used? _____

2. What fraction of juice is used in all? _____

3. Arrange the ingredients in order from least to greatest.

   _____

   _____

4. If a caterer makes 12 gallons of punch, how much of each ingredient is needed?

   a. water _____   **b.** cherry juice _____

   c. orange juice _____   **d.** cranberry juice _____

   e. apple juice _____

Probability

> **Probability** is the chance that an activity or event will happen. The outcome is the result of the activity or event. Probability can be written as a fraction:
>
> $$\frac{\text{number of a kind of item or the event}}{\text{total number of items or events}}$$

Example: What is the probability the spinner will stop on a star? Look at the spinner. It can stop on a star, a square, or a triangle. You can write a fraction for the probability of the spinner stopping on a star.

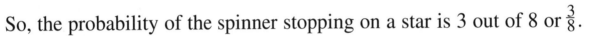

$\dfrac{3}{8}$ ◄— number of stars
◄— total number of shapes

So, the probability of the spinner stopping on a star is 3 out of 8 or $\frac{3}{8}$.

Directions

Look at the spinner. Find the probability of landing on each shape.

1. star

☐ ◄— number of stars

☐ ◄— total number of shapes

2. square

☐ ◄— number of squares

☐ ◄— total number of shapes

3. triangle

4. circle

Unit 3: Problem Solving

Fractions 3, SV 3406-1

Algebra

> A letter can take the place of a number in a number sentence. The letter represents the number for which you solve.

Example: $\frac{x}{4} + \frac{1}{4} = \frac{3}{4}$

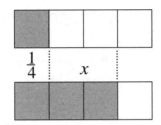

Step 1: Use fraction bars to show the known fractions.

Step 2: Compare to find what parts are not shaded.

$\frac{2}{4}$ is not shaded.

$\frac{2}{4} + \frac{1}{4} = \frac{3}{4}$

Step 3: Check.

$x = 2$

So, $x = 2$.

Directions

Solve.

1. $\frac{x}{5} + \frac{2}{5} = \frac{4}{5}$ $x =$ _____

2. $\frac{x}{7} - \frac{3}{7} = \frac{3}{7}$ $x =$ _____

3. $\frac{5}{6} - \frac{1}{6} = \frac{x}{6}$ $x =$ _____

4. $\frac{5}{9} + \frac{x}{9} = \frac{8}{9}$ $x =$ _____

5. $\frac{3}{4} - \frac{x}{4} = \frac{1}{4}$ $x =$ _____

6. $\frac{3}{10} + \frac{2}{10} = \frac{x}{10}$ $x =$ _____

7. $\frac{6}{8} - \frac{4}{8} = \frac{x}{8}$ $x =$ _____

A Fraction Message

Directions

Decode the message. Find the fraction in the boxes below that represents each letter on the number line. Write the letter of that fraction in the message boxes.

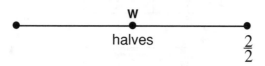

halves $\frac{2}{2}$

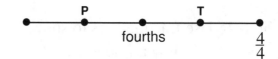

fourths $\frac{4}{4}$

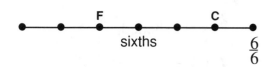

sixths $\frac{6}{6}$

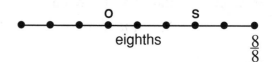

eighths $\frac{8}{8}$

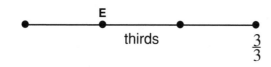

thirds $\frac{3}{3}$

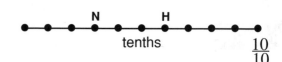

fifths $\frac{5}{5}$

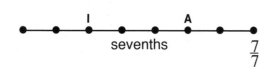

sevenths $\frac{7}{7}$

tenths $\frac{10}{10}$

The message:

$\frac{5}{7}$

$\frac{2}{6}$	$\frac{4}{5}$	$\frac{5}{7}$	$\frac{5}{6}$	$\frac{3}{4}$	$\frac{2}{7}$	$\frac{3}{8}$	$\frac{3}{10}$

$\frac{2}{7}$	$\frac{6}{8}$

$\frac{5}{7}$

$\frac{1}{4}$	$\frac{5}{7}$	$\frac{4}{5}$	$\frac{3}{4}$

$\frac{3}{8}$	$\frac{2}{6}$

$\frac{5}{7}$

$\frac{1}{2}$	$\frac{6}{10}$	$\frac{3}{8}$	$\frac{1}{5}$	$\frac{1}{3}$

Fractions and Decimals

A **decimal** is a number that uses place value and a decimal point to show a value less than 1. A fraction can name a decimal.

Example 1: Show tenths

3 out of 10 rods are shaded.

Three tenths are shaded.

The fraction is $\frac{3}{10}$.

The decimal is 0.3.

Example 2: Show hundredths

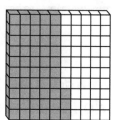

53 out of 100 cubes are shaded.

Fifty-three hundredths are shaded.

The fraction is $\frac{53}{100}$.

The decimal is 0.53.

Directions

Write the fraction and decimal.

1.

fraction _____

decimal _____

2.

fraction _____

decimal _____

3.

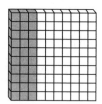

fraction _____

decimal _____

4.

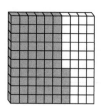

fraction _____

decimal _____

Money and Fractions

The value of money can be written as a fraction or as a decimal.

100 pennies = 1 dollar
20 nickels = 1 dollar
10 dimes = 1 dollar
4 quarters = 1 dollar

Directions

Write a fraction and a decimal to tell what part of each coin makes a dollar. Write the fractions in simplest form.

1. a penny

   fraction _____
   decimal _____

2. a nickel

   fraction _____
   decimal _____

3. a dime

   fraction _____
   decimal _____

4. a quarter

   fraction _____
   decimal _____

Directions

Write each amount as a fraction and as a decimal.

5.

   fraction _____
   decimal _____

6.

   fraction _____
   decimal _____

7.

   fraction _____
   decimal _____

Fractions: Concepts and Problem Solving
Grade 3

Answer Key

p. 5
1. C
2. B
3. C
4. C
5. D
6. C
7. C
8. A

p. 6
9. D
10. B
11. D
12. A
13. C
14. A
15. B
16. D

p. 7
1. 2/5
2. 5/8
3. 1/8
4. 3/5
5. 3 2/3
6. 1 1/10
7. >
8. >
9. Students circle the figure showing 4/8.; 2/4 = 4/8

p. 8
Students circle 1, 3, 4, 5, 8.

p. 9
1. 3
2. 0
3. 5
4. 8
5. 0
6. 8

p. 10
1. 1/2
2. 1/3
3. 1/4
4. 3/5
5. 5/6
6. 2/3

p. 11
1. 1/3
2. 1/5
3. 1/4
4. 2/3
5. 3/8
6. 3/5

p. 12
Check students' work to make sure they color the correct number of parts to show the fraction.

p. 13
For 1–3, check students' work to make sure they color the correct number of parts in each figure to show the fraction.
4. Students circle 3 of the 4 slices.

p. 14
1. shaded: 1; not shaded: 3; parts: 4
2. shaded: 1; not shaded: 2; parts: 3
3. shaded: 1; not shaded: 1; parts: 2
4. shaded: 2; not shaded: 1; parts: 3

p. 15
1. 3/4
2. 2/4
3. 1/3
4. 8/10
5. 2/3 of the kittens

p. 16
1. 1/2
2. 1/8
3. 3/4
4. 2/3
5. 3/10
6. 5/8

p. 17
1. 1/3; 2/3; 3/3
2. 1/6; 2/6; 3/6; 4/6; 5/6; 6/6
3. 1/5; 2/5; 3/5; 4/5; 5/5
4. 6/6
5. 9/9
6. 12/12

p. 18
1. <
2. =
3. >
4. =
5. >
6. <

p. 19
1. Students color 4.; 4
2. Students color 2.; 2
3. Students color 3.; 3
4. Students color 5.; 5
5. 2
6. 4
7. 3
8. 1

p. 20
1. 3/8 < 5/8 < 6/8
2. 1/6 < 2/6 < 5/6
3. 2/5 < 2/3 < 7/9
4. 1/4 < 5/8 < 9/10

p. 21
1. 1 whole + 1/2 = 1 1/2
2. 2 wholes + 5/6 = 2 5/6
3. 3 wholes + 3/4 = 3 3/4
4. 3 wholes + 1/2 = 3 1/2
5. 3 2/3
6. 2 2/6

p. 22
1. 1/2
2. 2/3
3. 3/4
4. 2 2/3
5. 1 2/9
6. 3 1/4
7. 6
8. 8
9. 4/5
10. 1/3
11. 1/2
12. 1/10
13. 3/4
14. 5/8
15. 3/5
16. 1

p. 23
1. 1/3
2. 1/3
3. 1/4
4. 4/5

p. 24
1. 2 2/6
2. 3 5/8
3. 4 1/4
4. 6 2/3

p. 25
1. 4
2. 3
3. 2
4. 3

p. 26
1. about 0
2. about 1
3. about 1/2
4. about 1
5. about 1/2
6. about 1
7. about 1 1/2

p. 27
For 1–3, check students' coloring.
1. 3/4
2. 7/8
3. 7/10
For 4–9, check students' adding.
4. 2/3
5. 6/7
6. 1/2
7. 4/5

Fractions: Concepts and Problem Solving Grade 3

Answer Key (cont.)

p. 28
1. 7 2/3
2. 10 2/3
3. 5 9/10
4. 8 3/8
5. 11 5/8
6. 4 2/3
7. 6
8. 6 3/4

p. 29
For 1–2, check that students cross out the correct number of parts.
1. 1/3
2. 1/6
For 3–8, check students' subtracting.
3. 2/3
4. 3/7
5. 3/8
6. 2/5

p. 30
1. 4 2/5
2. 5 1/2
3. 9 1/3
4. 1 1/3
5. 1 8/9
6. 4 7/10
7. 1 3/4

p. 31
1. tenths; 4 /10 and 7/10
2. sixths; 4/6 and 5/6
3. twelfths; 2/12 and 5/12
4. ninths; 3/9 and 4/9
5. eighths; 3/8 and 2/8
6. sixths; 4/6 and 4/6

p. 32
1. 7/10 + 5/10 = 12/10 = 1 1/5
2. 1/9 + 3/9 = 4/9
3. 5/8 + 2/8 = 7/8
4. 6/8 + 3/8 = 9/8 = 1 1/8
5. 5/8
6. 1 1/5

p. 33
1. 9/16 – 4/16 = 5/16
2. 6/8 – 5/8 = 1/8
3. 4/8 – 1/8 = 3/8
4. 9/12 – 9/12 = 0
5. 2/15
6. 1/3

p. 34
1. milk
2. 2/4 or 1/2 cup
3. Check students' shading.; 2/4 or 1/2
4. 4/5; 5/6
5. half an hour
6. 4 1/2 feet
7. 1/4 glass
8. cans; 1/4 more

p. 35
1. a book
2. 1/4 of the problems
3. 7/8 of the pizza
4. 3 1/3 cups
5. 5/8 of the trail
6. 7/12 slept in tents
7. 1/6 of the box
8. close to no juice

p. 36
1. a. The denominator increases by 1.
   b. They parts get smaller as the denominator gets larger.
2. a. The numerator and the denominator increase by 1.
   b. The parts get larger as both numbers get larger.
3. Students shade all 5 parts.
4. Students shade the first and third squares on the top row and the second and fourth squares on the bottom row.
5. 4/16
6. 2 1/2
7. 2/6
8. 5/14

p. 37
1. ; 4/4
2. X X X X X ; 2/4 or 1/2
3. ⊕ ⊕ ⊕ ⊕ ⊕
   1/8
4. ▰▭▭▭▭▭▭▭▭▭
   2/5
5. ▦▨▨▦▨
   8/16 or 1/2
6. ⊛ ◓ ◐ ◑
   8/16 or 1/2

p. 38
Check that students draw the minute hand correctly.
1. a quarter hour
2. three quarters of an hour
3. a half hour
4. a half hour

p. 39
A. 1/4 in.
B. 1/2 in.
C. 1 3/4 in.
D. 3 in.
E. 4 1/4 in.
F. 5 in.

p. 40
1. 2
2. 1
3. swimming
4. golfing
5. 29
6. a. 5/29
   b. 8/29
   c. 3/29
   d. 7/29
   e. 6/29

p. 41
1. 1/4
2. 2/3
3. orange juice, cherry or cranberry juice, apple juice, water
4. a. 4 gal
   b. 2 gal
   c. 1 gal
   d. 2 gal
   e. 3 gal

p. 42
1. 5/8
2. 1/4
3. 1/6
4. 2/5

p. 43
1. 2
2. 6
3. 4
4. 3
5. 2
6. 5
7. 2

p. 44
Message: A fraction is a part of a whole.

p. 45
1. 7/10; 0.7
2. 5/10; 0.5
3. 30/100; 0.30
4. 64/100; 0.64

p. 46
1. 1/100; 0.01
2. 5/100 or 1/20; 0.05
3. 10/100 or 1/10; 0.10
4. 25/100 or 1/4; 0.25
5. 50/100 or 1/2; 0.50
6. 56/100; 0.56
7. 95/100 or 19/20; 0.95